abc *of* aural awareness

ROY WILKINSON AND MARIA CHEN

Preparation for aural exams **Grades 1 and 2**

FOREWORD

The ABC of Aural Awareness is a collection of workbooks and cassettes designed to help pupils increase their musical perception. As with so many other skills, practice makes perfect, and the accompanying cassettes (one for each grade) should prove particularly useful in enabling pupils to practise independently at home.

There are three books:

Book 1 for Grades 1 & 2

Book 2 for Grades 3 & 4

Book 3 for Grade 5

Each contains a Glossary of useful terms, which will be appropriate for the Section D tests.

Aural Tests

Specimen books are available.

Aural Tests or Initiative Tests will be taken by candidates for all practical examinations.

For exemption see Regulation 6.

Introductory and Preliminary

Section A. Rhythmic Tests

1   Clap from memory the rhythm of a very short and simple melody, after hearing it played twice by the examiner.

2   Clap the pulse of a phrase, which will be played once by the examiner and then repeated while the candidate claps. The tempo may be slow, moderate or fast.

Section B. Pitch Tests

1   Sing a note, after hearing it played twice by the examiner. The note will be taken from the key of C major.

2   Two notes within the octave above middle C will be played twice as a melodic interval by the examiner. The candidate will be asked to say which was the higher or the lower note.

3   A short incomplete phrase will be played by the examiner and repeated. The last note will be the second or the seventh degree of the major scale. The candidate will be asked to complete the phrase by singing the key note of the phrase.

Grade 1

Section A. Rhythmic Tests

1   Clap from memory the rhythm of a simple melody in simple duple or simple triple time, after the examiner has played it twice.

2   Beat time during the second of two further playings, during which simple harmony may be added to the melody by the examiner.

Section B. Pitch Tests

1   Sing two notes from memory, after the examiner has played them twice. The notes will be chosen from the key note, 2nd, 3rd, 5th and upper octave of a major scale.

2   Identify 2nd, 3rd, 5th or upper octave from a major scale of C or G after the key chord and key note have been sounded. Candidates may describe the interval, give the actual letter names (the examiner will name the key chord) or use sol-fa.

3   Three notes within the octave above middle C will be played twice: the candidate will be asked to say which was the highest or the lowest note.

GRADE 1

TEST 1A

Tapping the **pulse** of a passage of music in **2 or 3 time**.
The examiner starts playing the passage, and the candidate must **join in as soon as possible** by:

(a) tapping the **pulse**, and

(b) **stressing** the **strong** beats.

(c) The candidate will then be asked to **state the time (2 or 3)**.

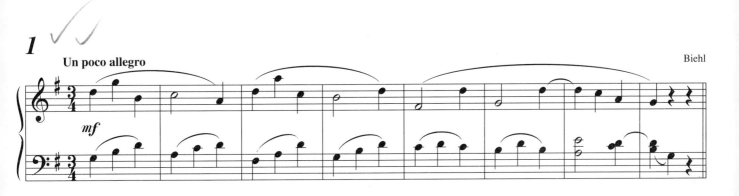

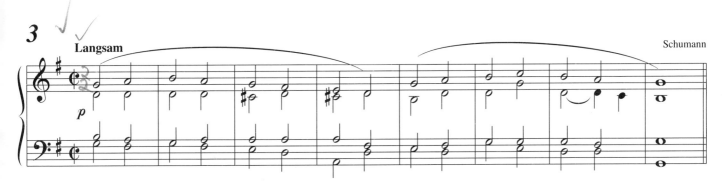

4

Moderato

Mozart (adapted)

5

Allegretto scherzando

Kabalevsky

6

Allegretto

Clementi (adapted)

7

Minuet

Clarke

8

Allegretto

Jenö Takács

9

10

11

12

13

Minuetto

Scarlatti (adapted)

14

Ecossaise

Schubert

15

Very slow

Kabalevsky

16

Andante

Tchaikovsky

TEST 1B

Singing (like an echo) **three short phrases** containing notes within a range of a major 3rd.

The echoes must follow each phrase **in strict time**, without a pause in between.

The examiner will first play the key-chord and tonic note, and indicate the pulse.

TEST 1C

Recognizing and **explaining** a **rhythmic change** made to a 2-bar phrase.

The examiner will first play the original phrase, followed by the **altered** phrase.

10

TEST 1D

In this test, the candidate is expected to know the meaning of the following terms, and to use them where suitable when answering a question.

GLOSSARY OF USEFUL TERMS

legato (leg.)	smooth and connected
staccato (stacc.)	short and detached
forte (f)	loud
piano (p)	soft
crescendo (cresc.)	becoming gradually louder
diminuendo (dim.)	becoming gradually softer

The examiner will play a short piece. The candidate must recognize changes in dynamics (*p/f*), tone gradation (*cresc/dim*) and articulation (*stacc/leg.*)

After the piece has been played, the examiner will ask questions about the piece.

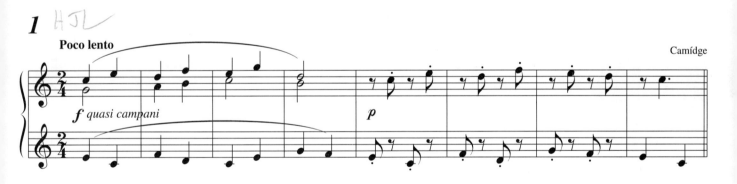

1 Poco lento

Camídge

1　(a)　Did the piece start loudly or softly?
　　(b)　Did it stay the same throughout the piece?
　　(c)　How did it end?

2　(a)　Were the dynamic changes sudden or gradual?
　　(b)　What is the Italian term for becoming gradually louder?

3　(a)　There are two phrases. Was the first one smooth or detached?
　　(b)　Was the second one played in the same way?
　　(c)　What is the Italian term for smooth?
　　(d)　What is its abbreviated form?

2

Simply

Macdowell (adapted)

1   (a)   Does the piece open loudly or softly?
     (b)   How did it end - loudly or softly?
     (c)   What is the Italian term for loud?

2   (a)   Did the music become louder gradually or suddenly?
     (b)   What is the Italian term for becoming gradually softer?
     (c)   Was there a phrase which became gradually softer?

3   (a)   Is this piece smooth or detached?
     (b)   What is the Italian term for detached?

3

Moderato

J. S. Bach (adapted)

1   (a)   Was the piece mainly loud or soft? Use the Italian term in your answer.
     (b)   Was it loud or soft at the beginning?
     (c)   Did it stay the same for the whole piece?

2   Was there a phrase which became gradually louder?

3   (a)   Was *staccato* used here?
     (b)   What does the word mean?
     (c)   What is its abbreviation?

4

1 (a) Is the piece mainly smooth or detached?
  (b) What is the Italian term for detached?

2 (a) Does it start loudly or softly?
  (b) Do the dynamics stay the same or do they change?

3 (a) Do any of the phrases become gradually louder?
  (b) What is the abbreviated Italian word for becoming louder?

5

1 (a) What Italian dynamic term could be used for the first phrase?
  (b) Was there any difference of dynamic for the second phrase?

2 (a) Both smooth and detached playing was used. Which of the two phrases was mostly detached?
  (b) What is the Italian term for detached?
  (c) What is its abbreviation?

3 (a) What Italian term is used when the music grows louder gradually?
  (b) Was there a part here which did that?

6

Andante   Weber

1   (a)   Is the opening smooth or detached?

      (b)   Was the ending smooth or detached?

2   (a)   Was the opening loud or soft?

      (b)   Did the piece end in the same way?

3   (a)   Did the music become gradually louder during any of the phrases?

      (b)   Did it happen more than once?

      (c)   Did any of the phrases become gradually softer?

      (d)   What Italian term is used when this happens?

7

Allegro   Scarlatti (adapted)

1   (a)   Does the piece start loudly or softly?

      (b)   How did it end?

2   (a)   Is there a phrase during which there is a gradual dynamic change?

      (b)   If you think so, was it a *cresc.* or a *dim.*?

      (c)   For what word is *cresc.* the abbreviation?

3   Is the piece smooth or detached?

8

Moderato — Clementi

1   (a)   Were there smooth phrases in the piece?
    (b)   Were there any detached notes?
    (c)   Was the first phrase smooth or detached?
    (d)   How was the last one played?
    (e)   What are the Italian terms for smooth? and detached?

2   (a)   Did the piece start loudly or softly?
    (b)   Did the dynamics change during the piece?

3   Were there any gradual dynamic changes?

9

Lively, strict — Schumann (adapted)

1   (a)   Is the piece mainly smooth or detached?
    (b)   What is the abbreviated Italian term for that word?

2   (a)   Does it start loudly or softly?
    (b)   Are there any dynamic changes during the piece?
    (c)   How does it end?

3   (a)   Do the phrases become gradually louder or gradually softer?
    (b)   What is the term for getting gradually louder?

15

10

1.   (a)   What Italian dynamic term is suitable at the beginning of the piece?

      (b)   What was the dynamic level at the start of the second phrase?

2.   (a)   Did the music anywhere become gradually softer or gradually louder? If so, which?

      (b)   What term is used when the music grows louder?

3.   (a)   Were the phrases mainly detached or smooth?

      (b)   Was the other type of articulation used? What is its Italian name?

GRADE 2

TEST 2A

Tapping the **pulse** of a passage of music in **2 or 3 time**. [$\frac{6}{8}$ time-signatures may be played, but should be identified as "2 time".]

The examiner will start playing the passage, and the candidate must join in **as soon as possible** by:

    (a)   tapping the **pulse**, and

    (b)   **emphasizing** the **strong** beats.

The candidate will then be asked to **state the time (2 or 3)**.

6

Allegro

Gounod

7 ✓

Quasi adagio

Bartok

8 ✓

Gracefully

Bach

9

Andante

Anon.

10

Animato

Beethoven

11

Menuet

Handel

12 Allegro

Spindler

13 Andante

Takacs

14 Allegretto grazioso

Mozart

15

Moderato

Le Couppey

TEST 2B

Singing (like an echo) **three short phrases** containing notes within a range of a perfect 5th.

The echoes must follow each phrase **in strict time**, without a pause in between.

The examiner will first play the key-chord and tonic note, and indicate the pulse.

23

TEST 2C

Recognizing and **explaining** a **rhythmic or melodic change** made to a 2-bar phrase in a major key.

The examiner will first play the key-chord and tonic note, then the original phrase, followed by the **altered** version.

10
Andante cantabile — Clementi (adapted)

rhythmic change

melodic change

11
Allegro — Scarlatti (adapted)

rhythmic change

melodic change

12
Moderato

rhythmic change

melodic change

13
Allegro non troppo — Tchaikovsky

rhythmic change

melodic change

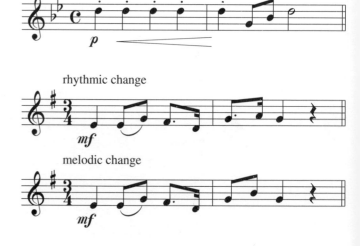

14
Andante maestoso — Holst

rhythmic change

melodic change

TEST 2D

In this test, the candidate is expected to know the meaning of some Italian terms, and use them where suitable when answering a question.

GLOSSARY OF USEFUL TERMS

Dynamics:	*pianissimo* (*pp*)	very soft
	piano (*p*)	moderately soft
	mezzo piano (*mp*)	soft
	mezzo forte (*mf*)	moderately loud
	forte (*f*)	loud
	fortissimo (*ff*)	very loud
Tone gradation:	*crescendo* (*cresc.*)	becoming gradually louder
	diminuendo (*dim.*)	becoming gradually softer
Tempo changes:	*accelerando* (*accel.*)	becoming gradually faster
	rallentando (*rall.*)	becoming gradually slower
	ritenuto (*rit.*)	slower at once
	a tempo	in time (return to the original speed)
Articulation:	*legato* (*leg.*)	smooth and connected
	staccato (*stacc.*)	detached
General (degree):	*molto*	much, very
	poco	a little
	poco a poco	little by little

The candidate will be tested on **one or two** of the following features:

—	dynamic contrasts	(*p*/*f*)
—	gradation of tone	(*crescendo*/*diminuendo*)
—	articulation	(*staccato*/*legato*)
—	tempo changes	(*accelerando*/*rallentando* etc)

The examiner will tell the candidate which of these features to concentrate on, before playing the piece. Then, the questions will be asked.

[The piece may be repeated in part or in full if necessary.]

1   (a)   Where is the loudest part of the piece to be found?
     (b)   What Italian dynamic term would be suitable at the end?

2   (a)   Do any of the phrases become gradually softer? If so, where?
     (b)   What is the Italian term for this?
     (c)   What is the abbreviation of this term?

3   (a)   Is the music mostly smooth or detached?
     (b)   Was the other kind of articulation used?
     (c)   What is the Italian term for detached?
     (d)   What is its abbreviation?

4   (a)   Did the piece stay at the same speed throughout?
     (b)   If not, where did it change, and say whether it speeded up or slowed down.
     (c)   What is the Italian term for this?

2

1   What happened to the dynamic level of this piece?

2   What are the Italian terms for becoming louder? and becoming softer?

3   (a)   Was there any change to the tempo? If so, what happened, and where?
        (b)   What are the Italian terms for becoming faster, and becoming slower?

4   Is the piece mainly *legato* or *staccato* in style?

3

1   (a)   Was the piece loud or soft at the beginning?
        (b)   What was the dynamic level of the last phrase?

2   (a)   Did the dynamic level change gradually or suddenly?
        (b)   Did it become louder or softer?

3   (a)   Was there any change of tempo?
        (b)   If so, where did it happen?

4   (a)   Was the piece mainly *legato* or *staccato*?
        (b)   What is the Italian abbreviation for *staccato*?

4

Molto andante e semplice

Grieg (adapted)

rall.

1   (a)   What did you notice about the dynamics of the first two phrases?
       (b)   What was the dynamic at the end of the piece?

2   (a)   Was the piece in strict time, or did the tempo vary?
       (b)   Describe how the tempo changed.

3   (a)   Did the dynamics change when the tempo changed?
       (b)   If so, was the change a gradual or a sudden one?

4   Was the piece mainly *legato* or *staccato*?

5

Con moto

Beethoven (adapted)

1   What changes from *legato* to *staccato* did you notice?

2   (a)   Did the music start loudly or softly?
       (b)   How did it end?

3   (a)   Were the dynamic changes gradual or sudden?
       (b)   What Italian term is used when the music becomes gradually louder?

4   (a)   Did the tempo vary?
       (b)   What Italian term is used when the music speeds up gradually?

6

Diabelli (adapted)

1   Did the piece stay at the same speed throughout?

2   (a)   Was it mainly *legato* or *staccato*?

        (b)   Was there any change or articulation? If so, where?

3   (a)   What was the dynamic level at the beginning?

        (b)   What was it at the end?

4   (a)   Was there a phrase where the music became gradually louder?

        (b)   Was there one where it became gradually softer?

        (c)   What is the Italian term for becoming gradually softer?

        (d)   What is its abbreviation?

7

Clementi (adapted)

1   (a)   Was this piece played in strict tempo throughout?

        (b)   What happened to the tempo at the end?

        (c)   What is the Italian term for becoming slower?

2   (a)   Was there a phrase which gradually changed in loudness?
       (b)   Did the phrase become gradually louder or softer?
       (c)   What Italian term is used for this?

3   Whereabouts in the piece was the loudest part?

4   (a)   Were there any differences of smooth and detached playing?
       (b)   Which Italian term describes the articulation in this piece?

1   Is the piece *legato* or *staccato* in style?

2   (a)   Did the piece start loudly or softly?
       (b)   Which was the quietest part of the piece?

3   (a)   Was there any gradual change in loudness?
       (b)   Did this happen more than once?

4   Did the tempo change? If so, say what happened, and where.

Reproduced and printed by
Halstan & Co. Ltd., Amersham, Bucks., England